SPORTS MAD

Contents

Match Crazy!	page 2
Tim, the Pest and the Footballer	page 12

Alison Hawes

Story illustrated by Ned Woodman

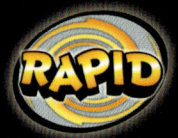# Before Reading

Find out about

- All the crazy things that have happened in sport

Tricky words

- crazy
- rugby
- referee
- golf
- butterfly
- matches

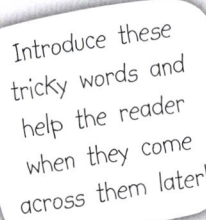
Introduce these tricky words and help the reader when they come across them later!

Text starter

Crazy things can happen in sport – in rugby, in football, in golf and in cricket.

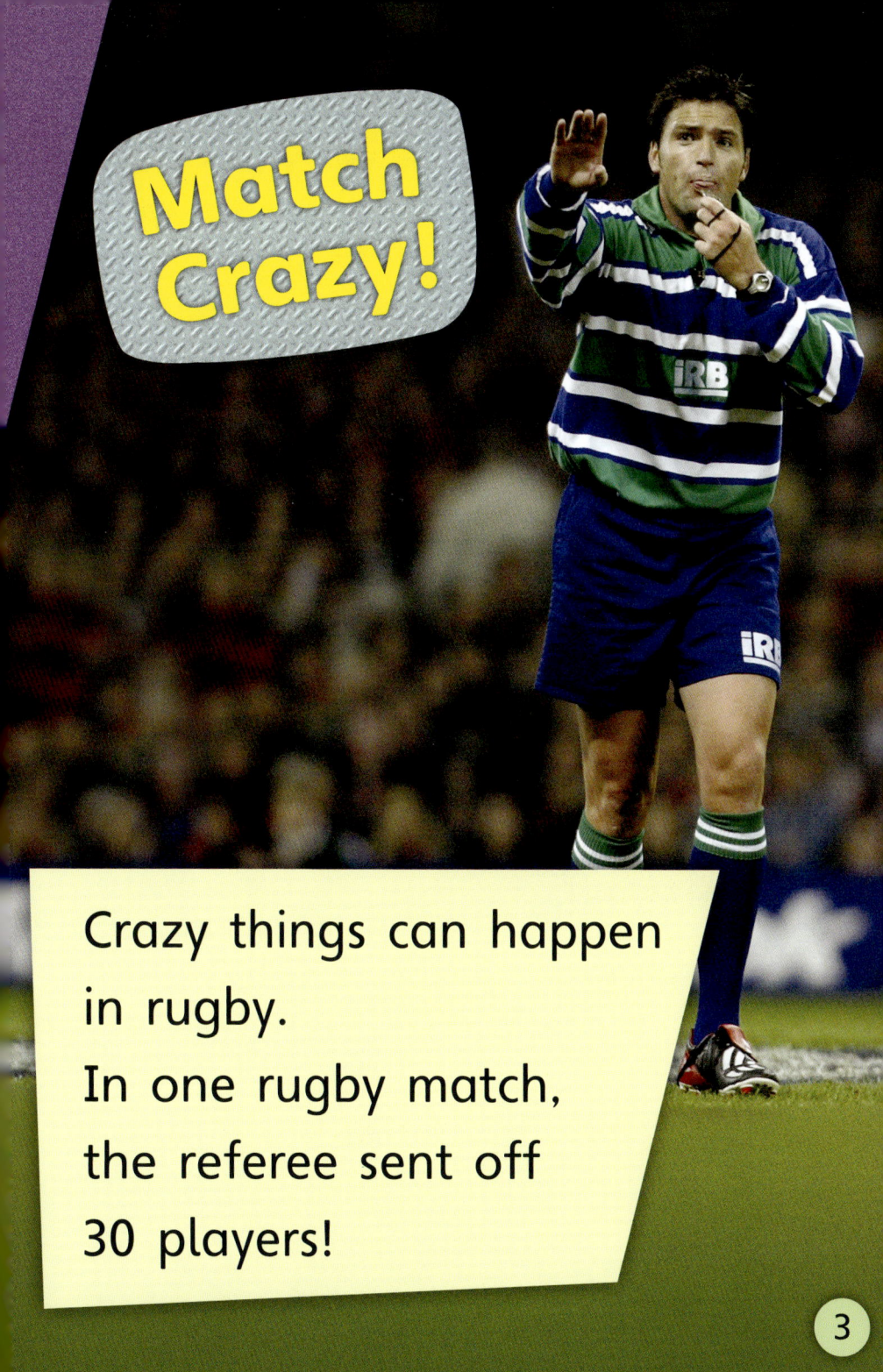

Match Crazy!

Crazy things can happen in rugby.
In one rugby match, the referee sent off 30 players!

Crazy things can happen in football.

In one match, a dog hit the ball.
The dog scored a goal!

In one football match, the referee sent off a player …

and the player ate the referee's card!

Crazy things can happen in golf.

In one golf match, a butterfly landed on the ball.

The butterfly sent the ball into the hole!

Crazy things can happen in cricket.
In one cricket match, a player hit the ball ...

and the ball hit a bird!

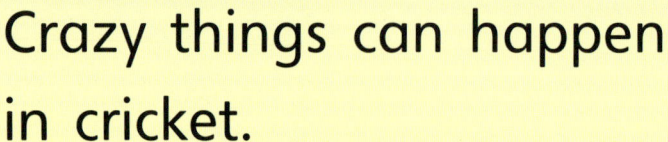

In one cricket match, the ball hit the matches in a player's pocket ...

Quiz

Text Detective

- Which animal scored a goal?
- Why was a cricketer's pocket on fire?

Word Detective

- **Phonic Focus:** Final letter sounds
  Page 8: Find two words that end with 't'.
- Page 3: Find a word with three syllables.
- Page 10: Find the words that mean 'burning'.

Super Speller

Read these words:

sent   off   one

Now try to spell them!

HA! HA! HA!

Q Why are babies fast swimmers?

A Because they're good at the crawl!

Before Reading

In this story

 Tim

 The Pest

 A footballer

Tricky words

- football
- shirt
- match
- watched
- pitch
- sorry

Introduce these tricky words and help the reader when they come across them later!

Story starter

Tim lives with his mum and his little sister. His mum is always making him look after his sister. Tim calls her the Pest. One windy day, Tim wanted to go to a football match.

Tim, the Pest and the Footballer

Tim put on his new football shirt and his new football cap.

The Pest put on her new football shirt and cap.

"I'm going to the football match, too," she said.

How does Tim feel about the Pest coming too?

Tim and the Pest watched the football match.

The wind blew and blew.

The wind blew the Pest's new cap on to the football pitch.

"Watch out!" said Tim, as the Pest ran on to the pitch.

What do you think is going to happen next?

"Watch out!" said the footballer, as he ran into Tim.

"Look at my new football shirt and cap!" said Tim.

"I'm sorry!" said the Pest.

"I'm sorry too," said the footballer.

"I'm not sorry!" said Tim. "Look at my NEW football shirt and cap!"

Quiz

Text Detective

- Why did the Pest run onto the pitch?
- Why wasn't Tim sorry at the end of the story?

Word Detective

- **Phonic Focus**: Final letter sounds
  Page 13: Find a word that ends with 'p'.
- Page 14: Find a word that rhymes with 'catch'.
- Page 19: What punctuation mark is used after 'Watch out'?

Super Speller

Read these words:

new   she   out

Now try to spell them!

HA! HA! HA!

Q: Why is Cinderella so bad at football?
A: She always runs away from the ball.